For Conor and Sadhbh
ED and JG

For Kate Janaki (Ella) and Dara Luca
SK

Chloe - the facts

The word Chloe is taken from the Hebrew, meaning 'green grass' or 'green shoot.' The name seems to have been in common usage throughout the eastern Mediterranean during the early centuries AD. Although Chloe is mentioned in the New Testament, the most likely source for the current popularity of the name is the classic Greek novel, *Daphnis and Chloe*.

The novel was written, probably in the 3rd century, by a Greek writer, Longus. Virtually nothing else is known about his life. The book, possibly set in the Greek islands, is considered to be one of the finest examples of Greek literature. It includes passages of action and description of idyllic surroundings, with consistent humour.

A timeless tale of fantasy, romance and rustic innocence, *Daphnis and Chloe* was first translated into English in 1587. The story tells of a romance between two young shepherds.

It immediately inspired a series of similar tales, including Robert Greene's *Pandosto*, dramatised by Shakespeare by 1611 as *The Winter's Tale*. In

Shakespeare's play, for instance, the shepherd complains "these boiled brains of nineteen and two.... have scared away two of my best sheep....if anywhere I find them, 'tis by the seaside browsing on ivy." This is believed to have been directly inspired by the reference in Book II of *Daphnis and Chloe* to young hunters and their hounds having "terrified the goats... which left the high ground and made a rush towards the sea and ate the green rope that the yacht was moored with."

There is also a Biblical Chloe, referred to in Corinthians, Chap. 1. She was a Christian who worshipped in the Corinthian (Greek) church. Although references are scant she is generally interpreted as having been a property owner or head of an influential local business family whose views were trusted and respected. According to the Epistles of Paul, she informed on 'dissensions' which arose among early followers of Christ.

The name became among the most popular in Britain and Ireland during the latter part of the 20th Century.

See *Daphnis and Chloe*, by Longus, available in a number of editions, including Oxford University Press.

Once there was a girl named Chloe. In Chloe's land there were trees and flowers, animals and birds, sea and mountains, ships and roads, just like where you and I live.

Chloe didn't live in a city. She lived in the countryside, high up in the mountains and beside the sea. She liked nothing better than to run through the trees, smell the flowers and listen to the birds singing. She often looked out to sea at ships sailing by and dolphins jumping from the waves. She waved to the dolphins every day. Sometimes she imagined they waved their fins to her in reply when they jumped from the water.

Chloe liked to play outdoors. She only came into her house at mealtimes. The fresh air made her feel very hungry. She knew that to grow big and strong small people have to eat their meals and not just the little treats that they especially like.

One day her mum said "Chloe, I have a special present for you" and she gave her the most beautiful whistle. "It's magic," her mum said, "someday it may save you from danger."

That was the one thing different about Chloe's world. There were magic things and sometimes magic things happened.

One of Chloe's jobs was to look after her mum and dad's sheep and goats. She made sure they stayed healthy and happy and were big and fat when they went to the market. One day, after her lunch she checked to see if all her animals were happy. She was just about to examine the magic whistle which she had put in her pocket when she saw a ship at sea.

It was not a normal ship. It was a pirate ship with a large, black flag flying from its sails. It was anchored very close to the shore.

"Oh no!" thought Chloe, "they are coming to steal my sheep and goats." Alas it was already too late.

Soon there were pirates everywhere. They had very colourful clothes and patches on their eyes. One hopped along on a wooden leg. He kept tripping over on the grass and shouting "Shiver me timbers, shiver me timbers."

When the pirates saw Chloe they began to make faces, to wave their arms and to swing their swords in the air. These were the tricks they had been taught in pirate school to make sure people are frightened by pirates. Chloe didn't know whether to laugh or cry.

Soon the pirates had taken all the sheep and goats to their ship. Chloe would not leave her animals. Then the pirates led her onto the ship also so she could not raise the alarm. She was very sad. Chloe took out her whistle and tried to play it but of course she had not yet learned how to play.

"I wish I could at least play you some music to cheer you up," she said to the sheep and goats. All the pirates laughed.

"I will play you music," said the whistle to everyone's surprise. Suddenly the air was filled with the most melodious tunes. The sheep and goats stopped bleating, Chloe stopped crying. The wind stopped blowing.

The pirates stopped laughing.

"We're trapped," they said. "There is no wind to blow the sails of our ship."

19

Then another magic thing happened. The dolphins that Chloe had waved to suddenly appeared. "We won't let the pirates take away your sheep and goats," they said. They pushed the pirate ship back to shore, where Chloe's Mum and Dad and friends were watching.

"We're in big trouble now", said all the pirates. One by one, they jumped into the sea to escape. Soon the dolphins had pushed the ship into the harbour and Chloe and all her animals were

safe again.

Chloe went home and ate a very big dinner. She put her magic whistle beside her on the table. "Thank you for saving me," she said.

"Thank you for being so loyal to your friends the sheep and goats. That was why my magic worked today," said the whistle.

What's in a name?

Usually centuries of history, religious or legendary tradition.

The main source of names is in religious history, in the names of saints (Catherine) and, post Reformation, in the *Bible* and *Old Testament* in particular (Sarah and Adam). The *Koran* provides additional perspective on many of these names.

Names from Celtic legend, like Conor, have recently gained increased attention internationally.

Another source is classical, from pagan, royal or literary figures, e.g. Lawrence (Latin) and Chloe (Greek literature). Historical figures, such as Victoria, also provide a rich source.

Then there's Jack! It probably deserves a category all of its own having appeared from nowhere - but perhaps from Jankin, a version of John - to become the ubiquitous name in fairy tales and now a highly popular first name.

Recently parents have become much more adventurous. This follows the decrease in family and religious bonds that resulted in names passing from generation to generation. Increased access to other cultures has led to 'name globalisation', with names like Tanya, Brooklyn and Chelsea now more popular.

Other names recall a particular individual or event. The *Bible* and *Koran* name, Aron, received a new lease of life - and spelling - from Elvis Aaron Presley. Jack